Ponds, Puppies and Ponies

Written by Margie Harding and illustrated by Shalayne Mowry

Animals, acres, ants,
Crawling on the little boy's pants.
Agriculture, ashes, alum,
He'd better hide his sweet crumbs.

Barn, butterflies, babies,
Just perfect for the ladies.
Birds, butter, bees,
A flutter in the trees.

Cows, crops, crickets,
Such music demands a ticket.
Climate, cultivate, cats,
Looking silly wearing hats.

Drought, ducks, dairy,
Don't mix to well with berries.
Dandelions, dyes, dessert,
Watch those thorns and stay unhurt.

Emus, erosion, equipment,
Quite the major shipment.
Eggs, elderberries, extracts,
All are part of the contract.

Farmer, furrow, forage,
I've got to have more storage.
Flower, fruit, fish,
Stored in my colorful dish.

Goats, geese, graze,
Are hard to see in haze.
Garden, grain, grapevine,
I think I've found a goldmine!

Harvest, harness, horses,
Some amazing mighty forces.
Honey, hybrid, hay,
My favorite place to play.

Insects, irrigation, incubate,
You wouldn't believe the growth rate.
Inkwood, itchy, inchworm,
Held in your hand, really squirm.

Journal, jug, jerky,
That turkey's really perky.
Jar, jelly, juicer,
It smells of a diffuser.

Knowledge, knots, knives,
Should I line up all those hives?
Kefir, kitchen, key,
It's time to climb the tree.

Llamas, lye, loom,
There's a skunk in the room.
Leather, livestock, land,
That likely wasn't planned.

Mulch, machine, market,
That patch up there is target.
Milk, mink, manure,
The air smells awful, sure!

Nutrient, nitrogen, nuts,
That chicken is a klutz.
Netting, nature, nettles,
She even trips on petals!

Ostrich, orchard, oxen,
Your rocks fill up the wagon.
Organic, ointments, oats,
I need a fence for all these goats.

Ponds, puppies, ponies,
The ducks in there, are phonies.
Post, pasture, planter,
Watch those critters scamper!

Quantity, quality, quarter,
That pig is sure a snorter.
Quilling, quart, quilting,
The water barrel's tilting.

Roots, ranches, roses,
Pink little kitten noses.
Rotation, rawhides, rabbits,
Chase mice, like little bandits.

Sheep, soil, sowing,
The tiny plants are growing,
Small sunshine seedlings,
Won't stay tiny weaklings.

Technique, turkey, tractor,
Bad weather is a factor.
Terrain, tilling, time,
This isn't mud, it's slime.

Uproot, ukulele, umbrella,
That rabbit is a little fella.
Upstream, uphill, udder,
The hail just makes him shudder.

Variety, vegetable, vinegar,
This puppy is a wiggler.
Veterinarian, violin, valley,
He thinks corn rows are alleys.

Wool, water, weather,
My lamb ran from the feather.
Weaving, wilderness, wildlife,
He thought it was a steak knife!

Xanthan, xenia, Xerox,
That was a really quick fox.
Xylitol, xylophone, xylocarp,
His legs were stretched wide apart!

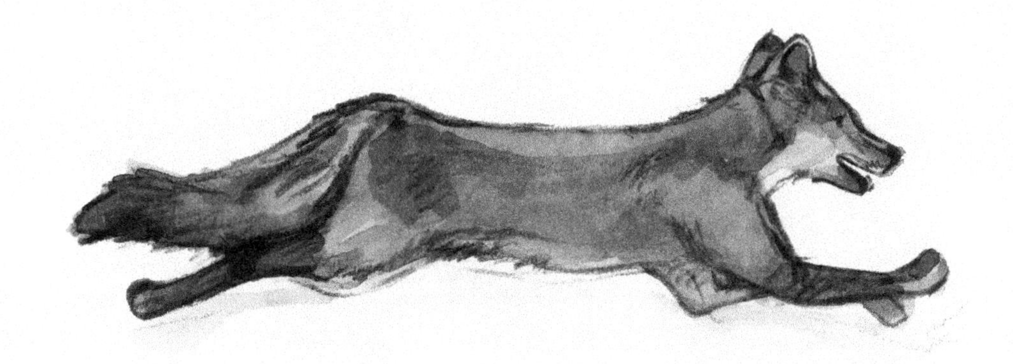

Young, yarrow, yogurt,
Look! That gopher's being covert.
Yarn, yard, yeast,
He's after a specialty feast.

Zeal, zone, zwieback,
Don't worry, I'll soon be back.
Zipper, zinnia, zesty
And when I do, I'll bring my bestie!

CPSIA information can be obtained
at www.ICGtesting.com
Printed in the USA
LVHW061654300322
714677LV00001B/6